Mother

[muh-thuh],
variation of 'Mater', in Latin.

To raise a child with care and affection. The giver of the best hugs and the source of the most unconditional love.

Prompt Journal

For

Mothers ♡

Daily Follow Along Prompt Notebook

Copyright © 2021 By Gold Wolfe Creations

A Letter For Mother

Loving words by someone who is blessed to call you mother.

Mother.
A word that can truly stand on its own.

There is no doubt the greatest person
in the world holds this title and carries
it well. But, how much is truly known of
her? What occurrences happened that
shaped and molded her into the
amazing person she is today?
It's about time to find out...

Mothers, you were either gifted this journal because your child/children deeply love you and truly want to get to know you; or you acquired this journal on your own because you want to get to know yourself a little more. Both are fantastic reasons to have a journal such as this.

Follow along and answer the questions in this journal to pull out memories and thoughts that might be forgotten or buried deep. Whether those memories brought you joy or discomfort, they are all important memories that have shaped you into who you are.

Sections included in this journal
All About You
All About Your Past
All About Your Future
All About Digging Deeper
*Positive Affirmations

All About You

What is your full name?

_____

Were you named after someone special? If yes, who?
If not, who named you and why did they choose your name?

_____
_____
_____
_____
_____
_____
_____
_____
_____
_____
_____
_____
_____

If your name were to be anything else, what would you want it to be? why?

_____
_____
_____
_____
_____
_____

All About You

Exactly how old are you today?

_____

Do you feel like your age? Older? Younger?
Give an example as to why you feel that age.

_____
_____
_____
_____
_____
_____
_____
_____
_____
_____
_____
_____
_____
_____
_____

If you could be any age, what age would that be? Why?

_____
_____
_____
_____
_____
_____

Date: _____

All About You

When is your birthday?

_____

As a mother what was your most memorable birthday? Was a good one or bad one?

_____
_____
_____
_____
_____
_____
_____
_____
_____
_____
_____
_____
_____
_____

What have you always wanted to do for your birthday but haven't done?

_____
_____
_____
_____
_____
_____

All About You

Do you currently have a significant other? What is their name? Are you two married and how long have you two been together?

_____

_____

_____

_____

What is your most precious memory that you have of your significant other?

_____

_____

_____

_____

_____

_____

_____

_____

_____

_____

_____

_____

_____

_____

_____

_____

_____

_____

_____

_____

_____

_____

_____

Date: _____

All About You

Where do you currently live? Home or apartment?

_____
_____

Do you rent or own? When did you move into your home or apartment?

_____
_____
_____
_____

What do you love most about where you live?

_____
_____
_____
_____
_____
_____
_____
_____
_____
_____
_____
_____
_____
_____
_____
_____
_____

All About You

Do you have any siblings? If so, what are their names and ages? If not, who are cousins or friends you could consider to be your siblings? What are their names and ages?

_____

_____

_____

_____

What is a memory you all share that you often think about?

_____

_____

_____

_____

_____

_____

_____

_____

_____

_____

_____

_____

_____

_____

_____

_____

_____

All About You

What religion would you consider yourself to be? If none, explain why.

_____

_____

How did you come to believe this? Were you raised in a religious environment or did you find your personal faith on your own?

_____

_____

_____

_____

_____

_____

_____

_____

_____

_____

_____

_____

_____

_____

_____

_____

Write one philosophical quote that relates to or inspires your beliefs?

_____

_____

_____

_____

All About You

What is your current hairstyle? How Long does it take to beautify?

_____
_____

What hairstyle in the past do you undoubtedly regret?

_____
_____
_____
_____
_____
_____
_____
_____
_____
_____
_____

What hairstyle / color have you always wanted to try but to afraid to get?
Why are you afraid to get that hairstyle?

_____
_____
_____
_____
_____
_____
_____
_____
_____
_____

All About You

What is your favorite food/meal that you could happily enjoy
every day?

_____

What is a meal you cook that is everybody's favorite but you could live
without?

_____
_____

What is a meal you cook that you wish you could cook more of?

_____
_____
_____
_____
_____

What meal have you cooked that went extremely wrong and family just
never seems to forget it?

_____
_____
_____
_____
_____
_____
_____
_____

All About You

What genre of music do you listen to the most?

_____

What singers/bands is your favorite in that genre?

_____
_____
_____

Have you been to a concert preformed by one of those favorite singers/bands? If yes, who did you see and what was most memorable? If not, what singers/bands do you want to see in concert the most? What one of there songs would be most exciting to hear and why?

_____
_____
_____
_____
_____
_____
_____
_____
_____

If you could take one person with you to a concert, who would it be? Why?

_____
_____
_____
_____

All About You

Describe your most prized piece of clothing. Why is it so special to you?

_____

_____

_____

_____

_____

_____

What is your all favorite clothing item to wear? When and where did you obtain this item?

_____

_____

_____

_____

_____

_____

_____

_____

_____

Has there been an article of clothing you received as a gift and you said you liked but you secretly you weren't a fan? What was it and from whom?

_____

_____

_____

_____

All About You

What car do you currently drive? What color is it?

_____

_____

How long have you had your current car?

_____

Are you happy with the car you currently have? If yes, why? If not, what car would you rather be driving and why?

_____

_____

_____

_____

_____

_____

_____

_____

_____

_____

What is the funniest memory you've had in your current car?

_____

_____

_____

_____

_____

_____

_____

All About You

What is your all time favorite delicious desert?

_____

_____

When was the last time you ate this desert?

_____

Describe the layers, flavors, and textures of your favorite desert in detail.

_____

_____

_____

_____

_____

_____

_____

_____

_____

Who introduced you to your favorite desert? What is the silliest way you can thank them?

_____

_____

_____

_____

_____

_____

All About You

Date: _____

What is your favorite hobby?

_____

_____

How long have you been interested in this hobby? Did it take long to learn?

_____

_____

_____

_____

How did you get into your favorite hobby – did someone teach you? If yes, who? If no, how did you get into this hobby on your own?

_____

_____

_____

_____

_____

_____

Is their anyone you enjoy your hobby with? Or, is there someone you'd like to enjoy your hobby with? Who and why?

_____

_____

_____

_____

All About You

What is your favorite television show? What Genre is it classified?

_____
_____

What is your favorite character and why?

_____
_____
_____
_____
_____

Does that character relate to you or any person in your life? How so?

_____
_____
_____
_____
_____
_____
_____
_____

Who introduced you to your favorite show? Do they like it as much
as you do?

_____
_____
_____
_____

All About You

What type of weather makes you feel most joyful?

_____

_____

Describe in detail the most memorable day you've had during your perfect weather. Were alone or did you share the moment with someone else? If so, who?

_____

_____

_____

_____

_____

_____

_____

_____

_____

_____

_____

_____

_____

_____

_____

_____

_____

_____

_____

_____

_____

_____

All About You

What is your ALL time favorite movie or featured film?

_____

What about the movies plot interests you so much? Does it relate to you?

_____
_____
_____
_____
_____
_____

If there was one thing you could change about the movie, what would it be?

_____
_____
_____
_____
_____
_____
_____

When you think of this movie, who is the one person in your life that comes to mind? Why is that?

_____
_____
_____
_____
_____
_____

All About You

After becoming an amazing mother, what has been your favorite holiday?
Why is it your favorite?

_____

_____

_____

_____

What has been the most memorable holiday as a mother? was it a good, bad
or funny memory? Explain in detail.

_____

_____

_____

_____

_____

_____

_____

_____

_____

_____

_____

_____

_____

_____

_____

_____

_____

_____

Date: _____

All About You

What is your every day or favorite perfume fragrance?

_____

When you spray your perfume, what does it instantly make you think of?
(person, place or thing) Explain in detail.

_____
_____
_____
_____
_____
_____
_____
_____
_____
_____
_____
_____
_____
_____
_____

Do you remember who first bought you this perfume? You should thank them
again! If it was you, thank yourself!

_____
_____
_____

All About You

What are your thoughts following "All About You"? What are some other thoughts you would like to share about yourself?

_____
_____
_____
_____
_____
_____
_____
_____
_____
_____
_____
_____
_____
_____
_____
_____
_____
_____
_____
_____
_____
_____
_____
_____
_____
_____

To the world you
are a mother, but
to your family,
you are the world.

All About Your Past

Where were you born? (City, State) Were you raised in the town you were
born in? If not, where is your home town?

_____
_____
_____
_____

What do you consider is the most memorable and best attribute of your
home town? And why do you think so?

_____
_____
_____
_____
_____
_____
_____
_____
_____
_____
_____
_____
_____
_____
_____
_____
_____
_____
_____

All About Your Past

What are the names of your Grandparents on your fathers side?

_____

_____

Where were your Grandparents from? What are the most memorable stories
you heard from them or from someone else about them?

_____

_____

_____

_____

_____

_____

_____

_____

_____

_____

_____

_____

_____

_____

_____

_____

_____

_____

_____

_____

_____

All About Your Past

What are the names of your Grandparents on your mother's side?

_____

_____

Where were your Grandparents from? What are the most memorable stories you heard from them or from someone else about them?

_____
_____
_____
_____
_____
_____
_____
_____
_____
_____
_____
_____
_____
_____
_____
_____
_____
_____
_____
_____
_____
_____
_____
_____

All About Your Past

What was the name of your childhood best friend?
At what age did meet you them?

_____
_____

What is an exciting moment you shared with your best friend that you will never forget?

_____
_____
_____
_____
_____
_____
_____
_____
_____
_____
_____

When was the last time you spoke with your childhood best friend?

_____
_____
_____
_____
_____

All About Your Past

Where was you favorite place to play as a child? Where was this place
located and who usually joined in on the fun?

_____

_____

_____

_____

_____

_____

_____

_____

_____

_____

When was the last time you remember playing there? What time was most
memorable?

_____

_____

_____

_____

_____

_____

_____

_____

_____

_____

_____

_____

All About Your Past

What relative did you visit the most often as a child?
How often did you visit there?

_____
_____
_____
_____
_____
_____
_____
_____
_____
_____

What is one the happiest memories you have while playing at your family
members home? Who do you remember playing with?

_____
_____
_____
_____
_____
_____
_____
_____
_____
_____
_____

All About Your Past

What is the name of the high school you attended for your senior year?

_____

What was your high school mascot?

_____

What is a fun memory you have that happened to you in high school that you _want_ your children to know about?

_____
_____
_____
_____
_____
_____
_____
_____
_____
_____
_____
_____
_____
_____
_____
_____
_____
_____
_____

Date: _____

All About Your Past

If you could go back in time to your high school years, what would you do differently?

_____
_____
_____
_____
_____
_____
_____
_____
_____
_____
_____
_____
_____
_____
_____
_____
_____
_____
_____
_____
_____
_____
_____
_____
_____

All About Your Past

What is a fun memory you have that happened to you in high school that you particularly _don't want_ your children to know about?

_____

_____

_____

_____

_____

_____

_____

_____

_____

_____

_____

_____

_____

_____

_____

_____

_____

_____

_____

_____

_____

_____

_____

_____

_____

_____

_____

_____

All About Your Past

What was the make and model of your first car? How old were you when you got the car?

_____
_____
_____
_____

What is a favorite memory you had in that car?

_____
_____
_____
_____
_____
_____
_____
_____

What is your last memory in that car?

_____
_____
_____
_____
_____
_____
_____
_____

Date:

All About Your Past

How old were you when you had your first crush? What was their name?

_____
_____

Where did you first meet your crush? What memory of this person sticks with you to this day?

_____
_____
_____
_____
_____
_____
_____
_____
_____

What advice can you give to your children about first crushes? If they are older, What advice should you have given them?

_____
_____
_____
_____
_____
_____
_____
_____

Date: _____

All About Your Past

What is the name of the person you consider to be your first boyfriend?
How old were you?

_____

_____

Do you feel like you learned a valuable lesson from this first boyfriend? If
so, what did you learn from the experience?

_____

_____

_____

_____

_____

_____

_____

_____

_____

Do you have regrets or embarrassing moments with or about your first
boyfriend?

_____

_____

_____

_____

_____

_____

_____

_____

_____

All About Your Past

What was your favorite subject in school and why? What grade were you in when you realized it was you favorite?

_____

_____

_____

_____

_____

_____

_____

_____

_____

_____

_____

Once you finished high school - did your favorite subject stick with you? Why or why not?

_____

_____

_____

_____

_____

_____

_____

_____

_____

_____

_____

_____

All About Your Past

Do you remember your childhood bedroom? Can you describe what your bedroom looked like in detail?

_____
_____
_____
_____
_____
_____
_____
_____
_____
_____
_____

Do you still have access to your childhood bedroom? If yes, are there any changes? If not, what is the last memory you have in your childhood bedroom?

_____
_____
_____
_____
_____
_____
_____
_____
_____
_____
_____

All About Your Past

Think back to your childhood of a fun or meaningful memory with your mother or mother figure. What memory comes to mind?

_____

_____

_____

_____

_____

_____

_____

_____

_____

_____

_____

_____

_____

_____

_____

_____

_____

_____

_____

_____

_____

_____

_____

_____

Date: _____

All About Your Past

Think back to your childhood of a fun or meaningful memory with your father or father figure. What memory comes to mind?

_____
_____
_____
_____
_____
_____
_____
_____
_____
_____
_____
_____
_____
_____
_____
_____
_____
_____
_____
_____
_____
_____
_____
_____
_____
_____

All About Your Past

Do you remember the address of your childhood home?

_____

_____

*What did your childhood home look like? What design element do you
remember the most and consider to be your favorite?*

_____

_____

_____

_____

_____

_____

_____

_____

_____

_____

_____

_____

_____

_____

_____

_____

_____

_____

_____

_____

_____

All About Your Past

What of your childhood home do you miss the most?

Thinking back to this home, what is a funny memory that stands out above all the rest?

All About Your Past

Who was your favorite teacher in elementary? Why did you consider this teacher to be you favorite?

_____
_____
_____
_____
_____
_____
_____
_____
_____
_____
_____

What's a school project that this teacher assigned to you that you remember to this day?

_____
_____
_____
_____
_____
_____
_____
_____
_____
_____
_____

All About Your Past

What was your favorite meal as a child? Who cooked this meal for you?

_____
_____
_____
_____
_____
_____
_____
_____
_____
_____
_____
_____

Have you ever prepared this meal for your family? Did they love it as much as you did?

_____
_____
_____
_____
_____
_____
_____
_____
_____
_____

All About Your Past

What is an instance that you and your family (i.e. siblings or cousins) did
something silly and crazy together and never got caught?

_____
_____
_____
_____
_____
_____
_____
_____
_____
_____
_____
_____
_____
_____
_____
_____
_____
_____
_____
_____
_____
_____
_____
_____
_____
_____
_____

Date: _____

All About Your Past

What was your first place of employment? What was your position and job description? How old were you when you go the job?

_____
_____
_____
_____
_____
_____
_____
_____
_____
_____
_____
_____
_____
_____

What is a fun memory you have while working at your first place of employment?

_____
_____
_____
_____
_____
_____
_____
_____

All About Your Past

How long did you work at your first place of employment?

_____

What is the reason you no longer worked there? Was it voluntary or involuntary? Explain why.

_____
_____
_____
_____
_____
_____
_____
_____
_____
_____

What is some advice you can give your child/children regarding their first job? If they are older, what advice could you have given them?

_____
_____
_____
_____
_____
_____
_____
_____

Date: _____

All About Your Past

What were you most afraid of when you were younger? Do you still have that fear?

_____

_____

_____

_____

_____

_____

_____

_____

_____

_____

_____

_____

How did you conquer that fear or how could you start to conquer that fear?

_____

_____

_____

_____

_____

_____

_____

_____

_____

All About Your Past

When you were a child, what career did you dream for yourself?
Did you make that dream a reality? If not, when did you no longer want to
pursue that dream?

_____

_____

_____

_____

_____

_____

_____

_____

_____

_____

_____

_____

_____

_____

_____

_____

_____

_____

_____

_____

_____

_____

_____

_____

_____

_____

All About Your Past

Was there a place where you and your middle school friends would often
hang out in your hometown? Describe it in detail.

_____
_____
_____
_____
_____
_____
_____
_____
_____
_____
_____
_____
_____
_____

what is the funniest memory you have in that hang out hangout spot?

_____
_____
_____
_____
_____
_____
_____
_____
_____

All About Your Past

What are your thoughts following "All About Your Past"? What are some
other thoughts you would like to share about yourself?

_____

_____

_____

_____

_____

_____

_____

_____

_____

_____

_____

_____

_____

_____

_____

_____

_____

_____

_____

_____

_____

_____

_____

_____

_____

_____

_____

_____

No matter how old
you get, sometimes, you
still just need a hug
from mom to make
everything better.

All About Your Future

To reiterate, where do you live? Do you own or rent?

_____
_____
_____

Would you consider where you live as your final goal/forever home?
If yes, describe the amazing place you call home.
If not, describe your dream forever home that you want for yourself in the future.

_____
_____
_____
_____
_____
_____
_____
_____
_____
_____
_____
_____
_____
_____
_____
_____
_____
_____
_____
_____
_____

All About Your Future

It's a true blessing to be a grandma - do you carry the title 'Grandma'?
If yes, what are their names and how old are they?
If not, do you hope to be a grandma in the future? How soon?

_____
_____
_____
_____
_____

What is the perfect vacation you would hope to take your grandchildren on
in the future?

_____
_____
_____
_____
_____
_____
_____
_____
_____
_____
_____
_____
_____
_____
_____
_____
_____

All About Your Future

Think about where you are currently in your life - particularly your <u>Mental Health</u>. Are you happy with your current choices in that area? What changes would you want to make for yourself for a happier healthier future?

_____
_____
_____
_____
_____
_____
_____
_____
_____
_____
_____
_____
_____
_____
_____
_____
_____
_____
_____
_____
_____
_____
_____
_____
_____

Date: _____

All About Your Future

Think about where you are currently in your life – particularly your _Physical Health_. Are you happy with your current choices in that area? What changes would you want to make for yourself for a happier healthier future?

_____

_____

_____

_____

_____

_____

_____

_____

_____

_____

_____

_____

_____

_____

_____

_____

_____

_____

_____

_____

_____

_____

_____

_____

All About Your Future

Think about where you are currently in your life - particularly your _Spiritual Health_. Are you happy with your current choices in that area? What changes would you want to make for yourself for a happier healthier future?

All About Your Future

What career or personal interest growth do you see for yourself in the next five years? What's the plan to get yourself there?

_____

_____

_____

_____

_____

_____

_____

_____

_____

_____

_____

_____

_____

_____

_____

_____

_____

_____

_____

_____

_____

_____

_____

_____

_____

All About Your Future

What is your ultimate dream vacation that you've always wanted for yourself? How and when do you want to make that happen?

_____

_____

_____

_____

_____

_____

_____

_____

_____

_____

_____

_____

_____

_____

_____

_____

_____

_____

_____

_____

_____

_____

_____

_____

_____

_____

_____

_____

_____

_____

Date: _____

All About Your Future

Is your self-confidence currently where you want it to be? What are some
steps you should take for yourself to become a more
self-confident person for years to come?

_____
_____
_____
_____
_____
_____
_____
_____
_____
_____
_____
_____
_____
_____
_____
_____
_____
_____
_____
_____
_____
_____
_____
_____
_____

All About Your Future

What currently makes you feel confident?
Make a list for your future self of what gives you more confidence and helps
you get closer to achieving your goals/dreams.

_____
_____
_____
_____
_____
_____
_____
_____
_____
_____
_____
_____
_____
_____
_____
_____
_____
_____
_____
_____
_____
_____
_____
_____
_____
_____
_____

All About Your Future

What do you feel is your greatest achievement as a mother?
(Not that everything you do isn't amazing)

All About Your Future

In your opinion, what would you consider to be the hardest aspect of being a parent? What can you learn from this difficulty that can help you be a better mother in the future?
(Not that you're not amazing already)

_____

_____

_____

_____

_____

_____

_____

_____

_____

_____

_____

_____

_____

_____

_____

_____

_____

_____

_____

_____

_____

_____

_____

_____

All About Your Future

What are your thoughts following "All About Your Future"? What are some other thoughts you would like to share about yourself?

_____
_____
_____
_____
_____
_____
_____
_____
_____
_____
_____
_____
_____
_____
_____
_____
_____
_____
_____
_____
_____
_____
_____
_____
_____
_____
_____
_____

All About Your Future

What future do you hope to see for your family, children, or grandchidlren?
Is there any way you can help them get there?

Mothers hold their children's hands for a short while. but their hearts forever.

All About Digging Deeper

What is the quickest way for you to lose respect for someone?

_____

_____

_____

_____

_____

Regrettably has there been anyone in your life who you've lost respect for?
Does this person know? How could they make it up you?

_____

_____

_____

_____

_____

_____

_____

_____

_____

_____

_____

_____

_____

_____

_____

_____

All About Digging Deeper

What is your best shower thought? Do you think of it often?

_____
_____
_____
_____
_____
_____

Have you ever made a major life choice based on a shower thought? Explain.
If not, have you had a recent major life change?

_____
_____
_____
_____
_____
_____
_____
_____
_____
_____
_____
_____
_____
_____
_____
_____
_____

All About Digging Deeper

What memory have you been thinking about a lot lately?

_____

_____

_____

_____

_____

_____

Is there anyone else associated with this memory that you would like to share it with? Maybe they think of this memory often too, what would you tell them about this shared memory?

_____

_____

_____

_____

_____

_____

_____

_____

_____

_____

_____

_____

_____

_____

_____

_____

_____

All About Digging Deeper

What's your current biggest worry? Either about yourself or a loved one.

_____

_____

_____

_____

_____

_____

_____

_____

_____

_____

_____

_____

Does this worry often affect your everyday thinking? What do you think can counteract your biggest worry?

_____

_____

_____

_____

_____

_____

_____

_____

_____

_____

_____

_____

_____

_____

_____

All About Digging Deeper

What do you consider the best decision you've made thus far in your life?

_____
_____
_____
_____
_____
_____
_____
_____
_____
_____
_____
_____

Who in your life was directly involved with this decision? Do you think they share the same views on the outcome? Why or why not?

_____
_____
_____
_____
_____
_____
_____
_____
_____
_____
_____
_____

All About Digging Deeper

What is the assumption that people make about you that's totally wrong?

_____
_____
_____
_____
_____
_____
_____
_____
_____
_____

Has there been an instance in your life when you corrected someone for making that assumption?

_____
_____
_____
_____
_____
_____
_____
_____
_____
_____
_____
_____
_____

Date: _____

All About Digging Deeper

What's something that you thought you'd have already done by now, but haven't? Why do you think you haven't done it yet?

_____

_____

_____

_____

_____

_____

_____

What is something that you have already done that you are surprised you actually did?

_____

_____

_____

_____

_____

_____

_____

_____

_____

_____

_____

Who did you experience this with?

_____

_____

_____

All About Digging Deeper

Who is someone you need to contact that you haven't?

_____

_____

Why do you think you haven't contacted them?

_____

_____

What is the last memory you have of you physically being with this person? Was it a good or bad memory?

_____

_____

_____

_____

_____

_____

_____

_____

_____

_____

_____

_____

_____

_____

_____

All About Digging Deeper

What was an experience you didn't think much about at the time, but it
ultimately made you a stronger person? Explain in detail.

_____

_____

_____

_____

_____

_____

_____

_____

_____

_____

_____

_____

_____

_____

_____

_____

_____

_____

_____

_____

_____

_____

_____

_____

_____

_____

_____

All About Digging Deeper

If someone were to sum you up with a phrase, what would that phrase be?
Can you picture an individual saying that phrase? Who is it?

_____
_____
_____
_____
_____

What past experiences/memories support the phrase that sums you up?

_____
_____
_____
_____
_____
_____
_____
_____
_____
_____
_____
_____
_____
_____
_____
_____
_____
_____
_____

All About Digging Deeper

Whether it be a person, place, or thing – what recent thing have you decided
that you're completely over and done with?

_____
_____
_____
_____
_____
_____
_____
_____
_____
_____
_____
_____
_____
_____
_____

Do you think you will change your mind about it in the future?

_____
_____
_____
_____
_____
_____

All About Digging Deeper

If you had to pick a single word to describe this year so far, what word would it be?

_____

Describe an instance this year that supports the word you chose.

_____
_____
_____
_____
_____
_____
_____
_____
_____
_____
_____
_____
_____
_____
_____

What do you hope to achieve within the year knowing how you feel about it thus far?

_____
_____
_____
_____
_____
_____
_____

All About Digging Deeper

Date: _____

If you were to devote your life to art, what type of art would that be?

_____

_____

Do you dabble in the type of art you chose? If not, why did you choose that type of art?

_____

_____

_____

_____

_____

_____

_____

_____

_____

_____

_____

_____

_____

_____

_____

_____

_____

_____

_____

_____

_____

_____

_____

All About Digging Deeper

What's a story about you being under intense pressure and how did you handle it? Was there anyone who experienced this with you and did they help the situation?

_____
_____
_____
_____
_____
_____
_____
_____
_____
_____
_____
_____
_____
_____
_____
_____
_____
_____
_____
_____
_____
_____
_____
_____
_____
_____

All About Digging Deeper

How often do you find yourself daydreaming? What activity are you
typically doing when you daydream?

_____

_____

_____

_____

_____

Describe a daydream that you had recently. Was it a daydream that you
wish would happen in real life? Why or why not?

_____

_____

_____

_____

_____

_____

_____

_____

_____

_____

_____

_____

_____

_____

_____

_____

_____

Date: _____

All About Digging Deeper

What's one thing you think you should be doing more often?

_____
_____
_____
_____
_____
_____

Describe a time in your life when you used to do that thing often. How did you feel during that time of your life? Is that feeling something you want to feel again?

_____
_____
_____
_____
_____
_____
_____
_____
_____
_____
_____
_____
_____
_____
_____

All About Digging Deeper

What are your thoughts following "All About Digging Deeper"? What are some other thoughts you would like to share about yourself?

No matter how old
you get, sometimes, you
still just need a hug
from mom to make
everything better.

Positive Affirmations

-positive phrases or statements that we repeat to ourselves-

I AM WORHTY OF THE
BEST THINGS IN LIFE

I AM A
BEAUTIFUL
PERSON

I believe
in me

I am enough

I am
confident
in my
decisions

Positivity is a
choice; I choose
to be positive.

I am
successful

I choose faith over fear

I deserve love,
compassion
and empathy.

I'm not my
mistakes

Date: _____

Positive Affirmations
List & Questionnaire

List four things you like about your face and skin.

_____   _____

_____   _____

List four things you like about your body.

_____   _____

_____   _____

List four people in your life you are thankful for.

_____   _____

_____   _____

List four positive things about your personality.

_____   _____

_____   _____

List four things you own that you are grateful for.

_____   _____

_____   _____

List four things that make you smile in the morning.

_____   _____

_____   _____

List four accomplishments you're proud of.

_____   _____

_____   _____

Positive Affirmations

Use the list from the questionnaire to write positive statements.

Write two positive statements about your face and skin.

_____

_____

Write two positive statements about your body.

_____

_____

Write two positive statements about the thankfulness of people in your life.

_____

_____

Write two positive statements about your personality.

_____

_____

Write two positive statements about things you own and are grateful for.

_____

_____

Write two positive statements that will make you smile in the morning.

_____

_____

Write two positive statements of accomplishments you're proud of.

_____

_____

Date: _____

Positive Affirmations

Write a list of positive affirmations that you need to implement for yourself
to maintain a happy outlook on life.

Positive Affirmations

Write a list of positive affirmations that you need to implement for yourself
to maintain a happy outlook on life.

.